For all children and adults who were affected by
the December 2015 flooding
and for the communities and volunteers who provided
invaluable help and support.

With grateful thanks to all those who gave their support so generously including:
BBC Radio Cumbria, Stephen Bolger, Borderloos & Event Hire, Brampton Skip Hire, Crosby Nursery at Laughingstock,
the Cumberland Building Society, Cumbria Community Foundation, Dappa Hairdressing for Men, Eden Flood Volunteers,
Roy and Joan Grimwood, Paul Hendy, Keith Mason Agricultural Engineer Ltd, Magic Mel,
the National Day Nurseries Association, News at 15, Newtown Road Day Nursery, NTC Joinery, Premier Electrical Ltd,
Rotary in Cumbria & Lancashire, Teacheco Ltd, Thomas Graham & Sons.

First published 2016 by Joellen Publications
© Sue Fox and Sarah Cooper
Images copyright © 2016 Irene Sanderson and Anna McKay

Catalogue record for this book is available from the British Library.
ISBN 978-0-9929949-2-1

Also by Sue Fox: *Joe and the Window,* 2013, ISBN 978-0-9929949-0-7
Joe and the Camera, 2014, ISBN 978-0-9929949-1-4

Printed by H&H Reeds Printers, Southend Road, Penrith CA11 8JH

Joellen Publications

Katie and the Floods

By Sue Fox from an original idea by Sarah Cooper
Illustrations by Irene Sanderson
with endpaper landscapes by Anna McKay

Katie and the Floods

After school, Katie was waiting for Mummy to finish work.
She was looking out of the office window.

Dark, grey rainy day.
Dark grey skies and sheets of rain.
Rain banging on the window.
Wind ripping through the trees.
Cars splashing through the puddles.
In the distance, the river swirling through the park.
People standing on the bridge watching.

Katie was worried. This is not a nice place to be, she thought.

Katie was glad to go home. She felt safe.
It was warm and cosy, as always.
Mummy and Daddy were very quiet watching television.

Heavy rain.
Fields of water.
People dragging furniture outside.
People brushing out houses full of water.
People climbing out of windows onto ladders.
People in boats.
Brunton Park football ground under water.

Katie picked up her rabbit and other toys and went upstairs.
She and the toys felt safer upstairs.
Mummy said that everything was fine, but Katie wasn't sure.
She wanted to ask about the rain,
but could see that Mummy was busy thinking.

Next morning Katie looked out of her bedroom window.
It was still raining but more gently;
just a tap, tap on the window
and little drops racing down the glass.
But ... water everywhere.

Puddles covering the road.
Puddles covering the pavement.
Puddles covering the path.
Puddles covering the soil.
Puddles covering the grass.

I like puddles but I don't like
these, thought Katie.

Mummy said that Katie's school was closed.
Water from the river had flooded the classrooms.
Everything needed drying out and cleaning.

This was all very strange.
Nasty strange.

She wondered if her PE bag and her favourite
fairy dressing up dress would be safe.
She didn't like to ask.

Katie's favourite things at school

Katie went to Mummy's office.
She looked out of the window. The sun was hidden away.
Everything was grey. Everything looked different.
The park had disappeared and instead there was a huge muddy lake.
The wind was blowing so hard, there were waves.

It's like the sea, thought Katie.
But I like the sea. I don't like this.

From another window Mummy and Katie could see further down the road which was completely flooded between the houses.
Cars were filled with water.
'It's a good thing that we are high up,' Mummy said.
'At least we are safe here.'

Katie was very quiet.
'I feel scared,' she said out loud.
Mummy gave her a cuddle.

After some days ... the sun was shining and it wasn't raining.
Most of the water had disappeared. Katie felt much happier.
She brought all her toys back downstairs.

Katie had a friend whose party had been cancelled because
of the flooding.
Daddy and Katie went to her house. Katie gave her a present.
They went a long way round as the bridge over the River Eden
was still closed because it wasn't safe.
There were a lot of people outside clearing and cleaning.

Katie's school reopened.
It wasn't the usual building, but portacabins in the yard.
Her PE bag had disappeared ... she didn't mind that too much.
The dressing up box was safe ... she would be able to wear
her favourite fairy costume again.

Katie played with her friend in the playground.
Everywhere spring flowers were peeping through the grass.

Mummy and Daddy laughed again.
They went for walks.
The houses they passed were dry and the builders were busy.
They went shopping as the flooded supermarkets
had opened again.

The bridge was safe for traffic.
Daddy drove over it singing, 'Eden Bridge was falling down;
we have built it up again,' ending with a loud 'hurrah!'

Katie was feeling back to normal ... well almost.

She still didn't like the sound of the rain and wind.
She was always glad when she got to the other side of
    Eden Bridges.
She wanted to know where Mummy and Daddy were
    all the time.

One day she told these worries to Mummy.
'In time it will pass,' said Mummy, 'and Mummies are always right.
You're right too, for telling me, so let's keep talking.'
'So we're both right,' laughed Katie, 'and that's good!'

Storm Desmond December 2015

In the first week of December 2015 homes and businesses across Carlisle, and the surrounding areas, were flooded for the second time in 10 years. Storm Desmond hit hard and an unprecedented amount of water fell over Cumbria. All previous UK records were broken. The met office said that the rain gauge at Honister in Cumbria collected 341.4mm of rain in 24 hours from the 5th to 6th of December. This is a month's worth of rain in one day. The water level of the River Eden recorded on 6th December was 6.2 metres above its average.

The result of this was devastating. Thousands of people were forced out of their homes by the water. Some were rescued by helicopter, some by boat, others waded through water that was waist deep. The army was called in to help move people to reception centres and search homes for the elderly or vulnerable. As the water level got higher so did the number of people evacuated from their homes and a major incident was declared. Across Cumbria and Lancashire 5200 homes were left empty.

It was a difficult time for everyone in the city, not just those that were flooded. Carlisle's Cumberland Infirmary was one of the victims of the huge power cut that hit the city. It had to run off a back-up generator. At the peak of the floods Electricity North West said around 55,000 customers were blacked out because a sub-station flooded.

In the surrounding areas some communities were almost entirely cut off because of water damage to major roads and bridges. The 300 year old stone bridge at Pooley Bridge was washed away entirely, effectively isolating the village from the south.

A major bridge on the A6 south of Penrith, Eamont Bridge, which is a Grade 1 listed building, suffered serious structural damage and had to be closed. Businesses in the area suffered, and many people faced miles of daily diversions around the storm damage.

On a slightly lighter note, Storm Desmond caused a national biscuit shortage, a ginger nut crisis. The McVities factory in Carlisle flooded, disrupting production. The factory employs 640 people and produces 80,000 tonnes of biscuits a year. The company said 40 million litres of water and 540 tonnes of debris had to be cleared from the factory before normal production could resume. Thankfully, on the 7th April 2016 the biscuit crisis was declared officially over.

Emma Borthwick
BBC Radio Cumbria